VOCABULARY GAMES

for Intermediate English Language Learners

Linda Schinke-Llano

National Textbook Company
a division of NTC/CONTEMPORARY PUBLISHING GROUP
Lincolnwood, Illinois USA

To The Teacher

The blackline masters in this book may be photocopied or reproduced using infrared copying techniques.

ISBN: 0-8442-7395-3

Published by National Textbook Company,
a division of NTC/Contemporary Publishing Group, Inc.,
4255 West Touhy Avenue,
Lincolnwood (Chicago), Illinois 60646-1975 U.S.A.
© 1987 by NTC/Contemporary Publishing Group, Inc.

8 9 0 ML 9 8 7 6

VOCABULARY GAMES

for Intermediate English Language Learners

CONTENTS

TO THE TEACHER

The enclosed set of 32 blackline masters contains 38 word games designed for intermediate students of English as a second or foreign language at the junior and senior high school levels. Intended as supplementary activities, the games can be used to review and reinforce everyday vocabulary, including verbs and useful expressions. Individual pages may be employed immediately following related lessons in basal series, or later as spot-checks to see if students have retained the information presented in daily lessons. Appropriate for individual as well as group work, the vocabulary games can be utilized in class or as brief take-home assignments. They are especially useful in the mixed-level class which is so prevalent in ESL programs. In all instances, the activities are intended to provide students with an enjoyable alternative for review and to save teachers time by supplying ready-to-use supplementary material.

Basal ESL series commonly used at the junior and senior high school levels were consulted in order to keep vocabulary and structures appropriate for the targeted groups. Whenever possible, items are presented in context in an effort to aid comprehension and retention. At times the context is deliberately cultural, since learning a second language involves learning a second culture as well. Generally speaking, the activities are arranged in order of difficulty, with more complex vocabulary and structures appearing in later pages. With the exception of crossword puzzles, all pages have directions and examples for the students. The majority of the games are self-correcting; in addition, answers for each game are provided in the Answer Key section of this book.

With respect to directions to the students, an effort was made to keep the language as simple as possible, especially in earlier pages. Certain expressions, however, are unavoidable. Therefore, it is suggested that the teacher include an explanation of key directional terms prior to assigning activities. Since comprehension of directions is crucial to completing assignments correctly, this preparation will help students not only with the vocabulary games in this book, but also with assignments in their content area classes. Words and expressions used frequently in the directions are as follows:

Fill in the blanks...	Plurals
Circle the words...	Verbs
Complete the sentences...	Opposites
Complete the paragraphs...	Contractions
Unscramble the letters...	Pair
Match...	Replace
Puzzle	Belong
Parentheses	Appropriate
Underlined words	Correct form

Six basic types of games are used, as well as combinations and variations of each. If students are unfamiliar with such word games, it may be necessary to work through the first instance of each type as a group activity. Types included are the following:

1. *Anagrams:* (See #1 as an example.) All anagrams are presented in context to assist students in decoding.

2. *Hidden words:* (See #3 as an example.) Such puzzles are based on a theme. Words in the puzzle may be found horizontally, vertically, and diagonally, as well as forward and backward.

3. *Fill-ins:* (See #4 as an example.) Fill-in items are presented in context and are self-correcting. Most fill-in activities are coupled with numerically referenced puzzles of sayings or sentences.

4. *Fit-ins:* (See #5 as an example.) Fit-ins are self-correcting in that incorrect words won't fit in the puzzle. In addition, most fit-in puzzles spell out a theme word when correctly finished.

5. *Inside words:* (See #29 as an example.) Words chosen are related to a theme. Students make new words by recombining letters of the cue word. Although many new words could be made from each cue, it is expected that students will find the most common letter combinations, so they are asked to make a minimal number of words for each cue. This exercise is useful in acquainting students with word formation practices in English, and teachers may wish to expand the activity if students are successful with it.

6. *Crossword puzzles:* (See #11 as an example.) All puzzles are related to a theme to aid students in identifying the proper words. The words "across" and "down" are used instead of "horizontal" and "vertical."

For more elementary or advanced classes, the author has created two companion books of blackline masters, *Easy Vocabulary Games for Beginning English Language Learners* and *Advanced Vocabulary Games for English Language Learners.*

ANSWER KEY

Master 1:   COLORS

1. black, white
2. Yellow
3. green
4. brown
5. blue
6. orange
7. gray

IRREGULAR PLURALS

1. women
2. mice
3. children
4. men
5. teeth
6. feet

Master 2:   DAYS AND MONTHS

Master 3:   GROCERIES

cheese
milk
eggs
fish
chicken
carrots
bread
bananas
apples
cake
Lets eat!

Master 4:   CONTRACTIONS

CAN'T
DON'T
ISN'T
DOESN'T
WE'RE
WHAT'S
COULDN'T
THEY'RE
I'M
YOU'RE
AREN'T
WHO'S
hidden word: CONTRACTIONS

Master 5:   BODY PARTS

head	nose
eyes	ears
teeth	neck
arms	hands
legs	fingers
feet	knee

Master 6:   FURNITURE

1. REFRIGERATOR
2. BATHTUB
3. RUG
4. PHONE
5. CHAIR
6. TABLE
7. COUCH
8. DRESSER
9. BED
hidden word: FURNITURE

Master 7:   FAMILY

son, daughter
sister, brother
grandmother
husband
wife
aunt, uncle
aunt, uncle
cousins, sister
brother
father, grandfather

Master 8: HOME ACTIVITIES

is playing, is watching
is cooking, is washing
is cleaning, is brushing
is sleeping

Master 9: SEASONS AND WEATHER

Master 10: NUMBERS

Across:
1. two
4. fourteen
5. thirty three
9. eight
11. seventy
13. nine
14. fifteen

Down:
1. twenty seven
2. forty
3. one
6. fifty
7. sixty
8. eighty
10. twelve
12. ten

Master 11: CLOTHES

1. watch
2. tie
3. umbrella
4. dress
5. purse
6. hat
7. socks
8. fan
The closet is full.

Master 12: PAIRS

1. saucer
2. eggs
3. butter
4. chairs
5. socks
6. eggs
7. sugar
8. coat
9. cold
10. husband
11. comb
12. knife

OPPOSITES

floor
happy
present
in front of
easy
little
after
hello
a lot of
wrong
noon
dirty
day
closed
hidden message:
OPPOSITE WORDS

Master 13: VERBS WITH TIME EXPRESSIONS

1. answers
2. washed
3. accept
4. practices
5. will study
6. admits
7. comb
8. watched
9. will wear
10. carries
11. helped
12. agree
13. will celebrate
14. tries
15. invented
Everything is correct!

Master 14: SCHOOL

1. bus driver
2. English, teacher, assignments
3. soccer
4. mathematics, history, boring
5. science, homework, exercises
6. library
7. bookstore, notebooks, pencils, classmates, practice

Master 15: OCCUPATIONS

Across:
3. deliveryman
6. dietician
10. doctor
11. carpenter
12. painter
13. dentist
14. milkman
15. gardener

Down:
1. electrician
2. accountant
4. architect
5. photographer
7. farmer
8. salesman
9. reporter

Master 16: SIGNS

left column, top to bottom:
stop
railroad crossing
telephone
pedestrian crossing
school crossing
ladies' room
no animals

right column, top to bottom:
picnic area
yield
no smoking
handicapped
no left turn
men's room
poisonous
go

Master 17: FOLLOWING DIRECTIONS

drugstore
post office
bookstore
home
Right!

Master 18: PRODUCTS AND STORES

1.	I	7.	E
2.	H	8.	K
3.	G	9.	D
4.	A	10.	L
5.	B	11.	C
6.	J	12.	F

HOLIDAYS

1. money
2. animals
3. purple
4. gifts
5. June
6. office
7. red
8. vacation
9. snow

Master 19: SPORTS

clockwise from top left:
football
track
ice-skating
basketball
roller-skating
baseball
volleyball
ping pong
diving
fishing
skiing
badminton
racquetball
soccer
gymnastics
golf
hockey
boxing
tennis
swimming

Master 20: IRREGULAR PAST TENSE

1. wrote
2. told
3. went
4. got
5. drank
6. gave
7. understood
8. had
9. came
10. ate
11. spoke
12. knew
13. saw
14. began
15. did

Master 21: TRANSPORTATION

Across:
1. truck
4. boat
7. bus
8. auto
10. drivers license
12. ship
13. car
14. ambulance
16. garage

Down:
1. taxi
2. chauffeur
3. motorcycle
5. train
6. horse
9. airplane
11. limousine
15. bike

Master 22: ENGLISH-SPEAKING COUNTRIES

1. New Zealand
2. Ireland
3. Canada
4. Scotland
5. England
6. Australia
7. USA
8. India

TWO-WORD VERBS

1. out
2. down
3. on
4. down
5. off
6. through
7. down
8. over
9. over
10. for
11. back

hidden description: two word verb

Master 23: GOOD, BETTER, BEST

1. strongest
2. worst
3. cleanest
4. richest
5. best
6. thinner
7. younger
8. drier
9. more valuable

DON'T BELIEVE
EVERYTHING YOU HEAR

Master 24:   DRUGSTORE

birthday card
calendar, comic books
magazines, newspapers
candy, ice cream
postcard, envelopes
record
alarm clock, cashier
sale, cheaply
aspirin

Master 25:   TOOLS

Answers will vary.

Master 26:   IRREGULAR
PAST PARTICIPLES

1.   bought/read, made, sung, stood,
     paid, bought
2.   lost, found, worn
3.   taken, fallen/been
4.   flown/been, been, brought/
     bought, said, shut, kept
5.   forgotten, slept/been

Master 27:   SOCIAL LIFE

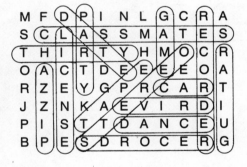

Master 28:   NEWSPAPER ADS

For Sale:
room, house
with, breakfast
and, family
fireplace
square, feet
garage, center
transportation

For Rent:
four, apartment
washer, carpet
living
bedroom
floor
basement
month

Wanted:
building
minutes
north
evenings

For Sale:
door
sedan
miles per gallon
air conditioning

You can find anything
in the newspaper.

Master 29:   EXPRESSIONS

1.   dogs
2.   low
3.   stop
4.   water
5.   back
6.   thin
7.   out
8.   down
9.   left
10.   take
11.   short
12.   go

FEELINGS

Answers will vary.

Master 30: JOB HUNTING

Across:
1. check
6. application
9. employer
10. birth
12. sex
13. hire
14. days
15. weight

Down:
2. employee
3. interview
4. job
5. weekend
7. part
8. height
11. hours

Master 31: OTHER WAYS OF SAYING THINGS I

1. got out of
2. call you up
3. get better
4. went back
5. fill out
6. looked through
7. got in
8. got sick

OTHER WAYS OF SAYING THINGS II

1. call me up
2. write me
3. very tired
4. quit
5. contact him
6. Come over

Master 32: EMERGENCIES

help
dentist
broken, doctor, fire
department, police
accident, hospital
phone, book
operator, Neighbors

```
D  N  O  H  B  P  M  I  E  A
D  E  P  A  R  T  M  E  N  T
F  I  E  L  O  V  R  O  N  S
I  G  R  S  K  P  L  E  H  I
R  H  A  W  E  X  D  Y  N  T
E  B  T  O  N  I  U  T  J  N
B  O  O  K  C  P  H  O  N  E
K  R  B  C  R  O  T  C  O  D
G  S  A  P  O  L  I  C  E  B
C  H  O  S  P  I  T  A  L  F
```

1. COLORS

DIRECTIONS: Unscramble the letters to make a word. Write the word in the blank.

Example: Fire engines are _____red_____ .
                                              erd

1. Zebras are _____ and _____ .
                      kacbl   tewih

2. _____ roses are my favorite flowers.
        weloly

3. Grass is _____ in the summer.
                    nereg

4. I like your new _____ shoes.
                          worbn

5. Susan has _____ eyes.
                    uleb

6. Mark drives an _____ car.
                          regona

7. His _____
            yarg

2. IRREGULAR PLURALS

DIRECTIONS: Write the plurals of the following words in the blanks. Then write the words in the puzzle.

Example: leaf   ___leaves___

1. woman   _____

2. mouse   _____

3. child   _____

4. man   _____

5. tooth   _____

6. foot   _____

3. DAYS AND MONTHS

DIRECTIONS: Find the seven days of the week and the twelve months of the year in the puzzle and circle them.

```
C D E F Y X Y Z B H R
O R A B A P Q R S T Q
C Y M E D F G D O G P
Y R A U N A J E C F O
A A R J U N E C T C V
U U C N S O A E O D M
G R H Y B V Z M B E F
U B A N A E Y B E A R
S E P T E M B E R W P
T F R K C B O R I V O
A T I L D E Y N J U Q
J U L Y X R A H D K M
W E D N E S D A Y A L
B S D S I T I G W K Y
O D E T H U R S D A Y
P A F R J U F H V L S
Q Y A D R U T A S M T
```

APRIL MONDAY JANUARY WEDNESDAY AUGUST THURSDAY

FEBRUARY

MAY · FRIDAY · DECEMBER

OCTOBER · SUNDAY · JUNE TUESDAY · MARCH

SEPTEMBER SATURDAY · JULY · NOVEMBER

4. GROCERIES

DIRECTIONS: Fill in the blanks with the word that matches the picture. Then write the correct letters in the numbered blanks at the bottom of the page.

SHOPPING LIST

___ ___ ___ ___ ___ ___
1   11   21   31   41   47

___ ___ ___ ___
2   12   22   32

___ ___ ___ ___
3   13   23   33

___ ___ ___ ___
4   14   24   34

___ ___ ___ ___ ___ ___ ___
5   15   25   35   42   48   52

___ ___ ___ ___ ___ ___ ___
6   16   26   36   43   49   53

___ ___ ___ ___ ___
7   17   27   37   44

___ ___ ___ ___ ___ ___ ___
8   18   28   38   45   50   54

___ ___ ___ ___ ___ ___
9   19   29   39   46   51

___ ___ ___ ___
10   20   30   40

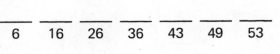

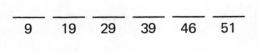

___ ___ ___ ___   ___ ___ ___!
39   21   49   33   40   9   49

5. CONTRACTIONS

DIRECTIONS: Fill in the blanks with the contraction of the underlined words. Then read the hidden word above the arrow.

Example: He is a student.

| H | E' | S |

He can not sing.

I do not like pizza.

It is not humid today.

She does not want coffee.

We are close friends.

What is his name?

They could not do the problem.

They are cousins.

I am tired.

You are a good dancer.

We are not hungry.

Who is the new student?

↑
hidden word

6. BODY PARTS

DIRECTIONS: Fill in the blanks with the correct words.

News Flash!!   A spaceship landed today.
This is a picture of the pilot.

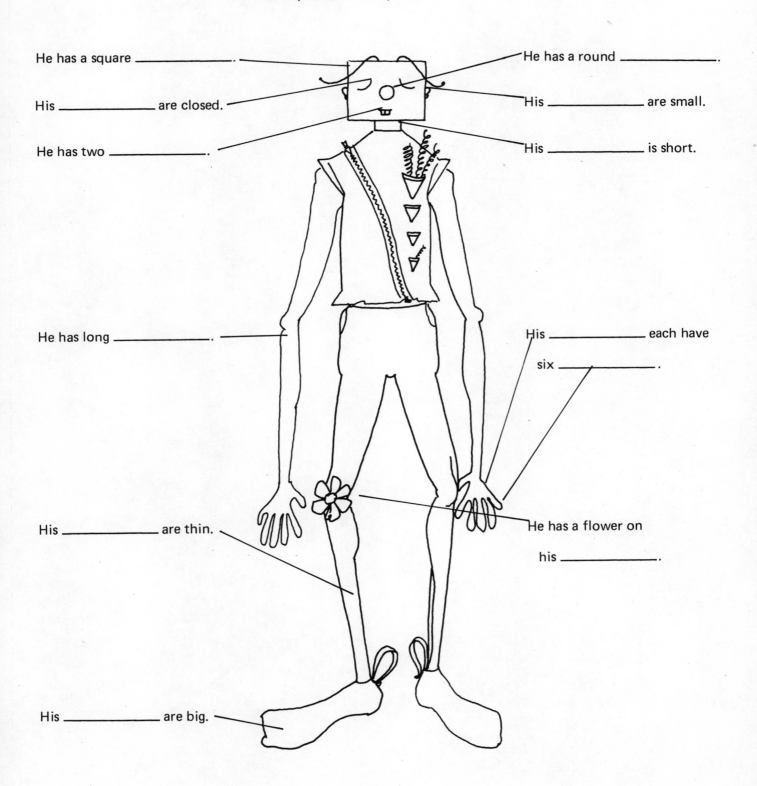

He has a square _____.

His _____ are closed.

He has two _____.

He has long _____.

His _____ are thin.

His _____ are big.

He has a round _____.

His _____ are small.

His _____ is short.

His _____ each have

six _____.

He has a flower on

his _____.

7. FURNITURE

DIRECTIONS: Fill in the blanks with the words at the bottom of the page to find the hidden word above the arrow that describes them all.

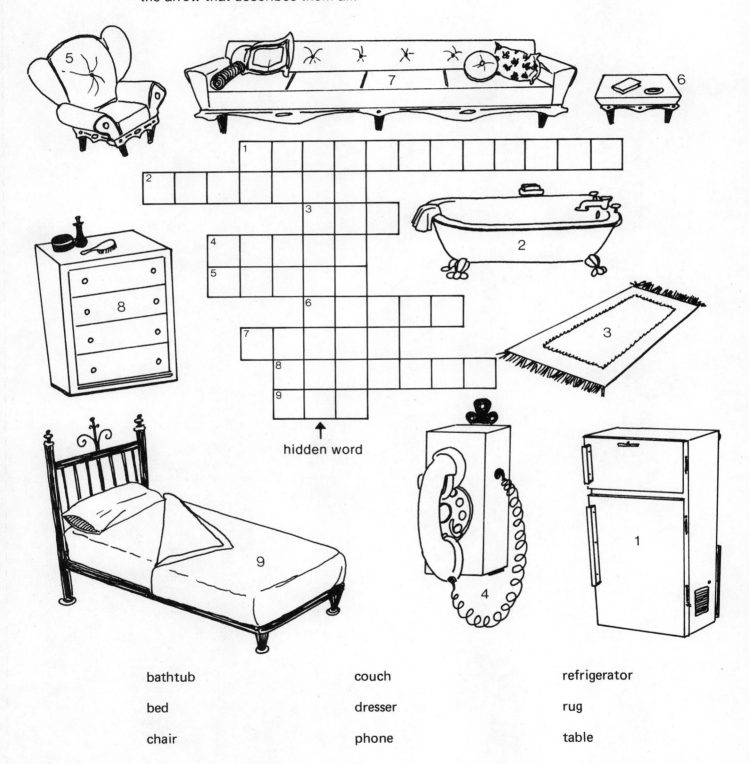

hidden word

bathtub   couch   refrigerator

bed   dresser   rug

chair   phone   table

8. FAMILY

DIRECTIONS: Look at the family tree. Then read the paragraph and fill in the blanks correctly. Names of family members are given below the family tree.

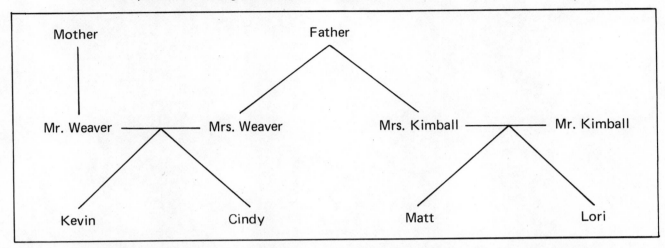

Family members: husband, wife, son, daughter, aunt, uncle, sister, brother, cousins, grandfather, grandmother, father

Mr. and Mrs. Weaver are married. They have two children, a boy, Kevin, and a girl, Cindy. Kevin is Mr. and Mrs. Weaver's _____. Cindy is their _____. Cindy is Kevin's _____. Kevin is Cindy's _____. Mr. Weaver's mother lives with the Weavers. She is Kevin and Cindy's _____. Mrs. Weaver's sister, Mrs. Kimball, sometimes brings her family to visit the Weavers. Mrs. Kimball is married to Mr. Kimball. He is her _____. She is his _____. Mr. and Mrs. Kimball also have two children, a boy, Matt, and a girl, Lori. Mrs. Weaver is Matt and Lori's _____. Mr. Weaver is their _____. Mrs. Kimball is Kevin and Cindy's _____. Mr. Kimball is their _____. Cindy and Kevin are Matt and Lori's _____. Lori is Matt's _____. Matt is Lori's _____. Sometimes Mrs. Kimball brings her father to the Weavers' house. Mrs. Kimball's father is also Mrs. Weaver's _____. He is the _____ of all four children.

We are different things to different people.

9. HOME ACTIVITIES

DIRECTIONS: Look at the picture. Fill in the blanks with the correct form of the verbs at the bottom of the page.

Example: The dog _____is eating_____ his food.

It's Saturday. The Schultz family is at home. Everyone is doing something. Mrs. Schultz

_____ the piano in the living room, and Grandpa _____ TV.

In the kitchen, Maria _____ , and Peter _____ the dishes.

Mr. Schultz _____ the garage. Grandma _____ her hair in the

bathroom. The baby _____ in the bedroom.

brush	eat	sit
clean	listen	sleep
cook	play	wash
drink	read	watch

10. SEASONS AND WEATHER

DIRECTIONS: Find the underlined words in the puzzle.

Alice: What's the <u>weather</u> like today?

Karen: It's <u>cloudy</u> and <u>cold</u>. I think it's going to <u>snow</u>.

Alice: Good. I like <u>winter</u>.

Karen: I don't. I like <u>spring</u>. Then it's <u>windy</u> and <u>rainy</u>. I love <u>summer</u>, too. Then it's <u>hot</u> and <u>sunny</u>.

Alice: My favorite <u>season</u> is <u>fall</u>. Sometimes it's <u>foggy</u> in the morning, but the days are always <u>mild</u>.

```
S N O W A B D X
L J S P R I N G
G R E M M U S W
W E A T H E R I
D H S U N N Y N
L F O G G Y N D
O A N T Y C I Y
C L O U D Y A H
D L I M Z E R I
F W I N T E R K
```

11. NUMBERS

DIRECTIONS: Fill in the puzzle with the correct answers.

Example: Two plus two | F | O | U | R |

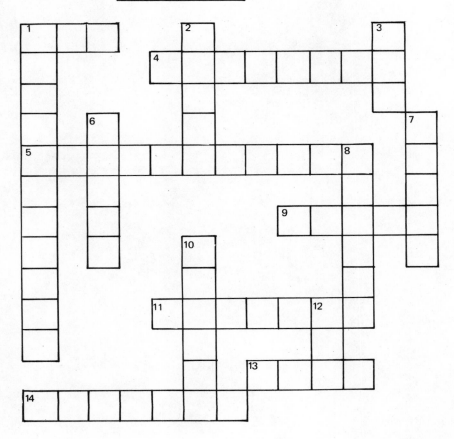

Across

1. fifty divided by twenty-five
4. seven times two
5. eleven times three
9. thirty-two divided by four
11. eighty-three minus thirteen
13. eighteen minus nine
14. three times five

Down

1. nine times three
2. ninety-two minus fifty-two
3. one hundred minus ninety-nine
6. thirty-seven plus thirteen
7. fifteen times four
8. fifty-four plus twenty-six
10. thirty-six divided by three
12. six plus four

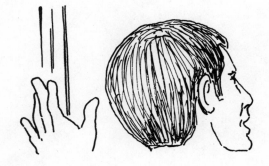

12. CLOTHES

DIRECTIONS: Circle the word that does <u>not</u> belong with the others. Write each circled word in the blanks below. Then fill in the blanks at the bottom of the page with the correct letters.

Example: dog   cat   bird    car

1. coat   watch   gloves   boots

2. tie   skirt   blouse   dress

3. ice skates   golf shoes   umbrella   tennis shoes

4. pants   shirt   tie   dress

5. sweater   purse   jacket   raincoat

6. shoes   socks   hat   boots

7. watch   bracelet   ring   socks

8. fan   pants   shorts   jeans

1. __ __ __ __ __ __ __
  49 41 33 25 17 9 1

2. __ __ __ __ __ __ __
  50 42 34 26 18 10 2

3. __ __ __ __ __ __ __ __ __ __ __
  62 61 60 58 55 51 43 35 27 19 11 3

4. __ __ __ __ __ __
  44 36 28 20 12 4

5. __ __ __ __ __ __ __ __
  56 52 45 37 29 21 13 5

6. __ __ __ __ __ __
  46 38 30 22 14 6

7. __ __ __ __ __ __ __ __ __
  59 57 53 47 39 31 23 15 7

8. __ __ __ __ __ __ __
  54 48 40 32 24 16 8

__ __ __   __ __ __ __ __ __ __   __ __   __ __ __ __ .
33 46 29   25 51 57 20 34 50   42 12   54 62 51 43

13. PAIRS

DIRECTIONS: Write in the blanks a word that makes a pair with the underlined word.

Example: He has a new ball and _b_ _a_ _t_.

1. The cup and _ _ _ _ _ _ are broken.

2. I'll have bacon and _ _ _ _.

3. Pass the bread and _ _ _ _ _ _.

4. Mom wants a new dining room table and _ _ _ _ _ _.

5. My shoes and _ _ _ _ _ _ are under the bed.

6. He likes ham and _ _ _ _ for breakfast.

7. I take cream and _ _ _ _ _ in my coffee.

8. He forgot his hat and _ _ _ _.

9. The cabin has hot and _ _ _ _ running water.

10. Sam and Helen are _ _ _ _ _ _ _ and wife.

11. I forgot to pack my brush and _ _ _ _.

12. Waiter, please bring me a _ _ _ _ _ and fork.

14. OPPOSITES

DIRECTIONS: Write in the blanks a word that is the opposite of the word at the left. Then read the hidden message above the arrow.

Example: come | G | O |

ceiling

sad

absent

behind

hard (test)

big

before

goodbye

a little of

right

midnight

clean

night

open

↑
hidden message

Name _____ Date _____ Master 13

15. VERBS WITH TIME EXPRESSIONS

DIRECTIONS: Fill in the blanks with the correct form of the verb in parentheses. Then fill in the blanks at the bottom of the page with the correct letters.

Example: My brother <u>l i k e s</u> baseball. (like)

1. Carl usually __ __ __ __ __ __ the questions correctly. (answer)

1

2. I __ __ __ __ __ our new car yesterday. (wash)

3

3. Will you __ __ __ __ __ __ my apology? (accept)

13

4. My brother __ __ __ __ __ __ __ __ piano every day. (practice)

4

5. They __ __ __ __ __ __ __ __ at the university next year. (study)

5

6. My sister sometimes __ __ __ __ __ __ she is wrong. (admit)

6

7. Did you __ __ __ __ your hair this morning? (comb)

14

8. Last night we all __ __ __ __ __ __ __ the football game. (watch)

7

9. Tomorrow I __ __ __ __ __ __ __ __ my new outfit. (wear)

8   15

10. My father never __ __ __ __ __ __ __ an umbrella. (carry)

16

11. He __ __ __ __ __ __ the neighbors last week. (help)

17

12. Do you __ __ __ __ __ with me? (agree)

10

13. They __ __ __ __ __ __ __ __ __ __ __ their anniversary next month. (celebrate)

11   18

14. Olga __ __ __ __ __ to help her mother every day. (try)

19   12

15. Edison __ __ __ __ __ __ __ __ the light bulb. (invent)

2   9

__ __ __ __ __ __ __ __ __ __ __ __ __ __ __ __ __ __ __!

1 2 3 4 5 6 7 8 9 10 11 12 13 14 15 16 17 18 19

© National Textbook Company

16. SCHOOL

DIRECTIONS: Unscramble the letters to make a word.

Example: I was late for ____class____ today.
slacs

1. The _____ picks me up at 7:30 every morning.
   sub verird

2. My first class is _____. The _____ gives a lot of _____.
   shiglen   cehaetr   snetmsagins

3. Then I have gym class. _____ is my favorite sport.
   crocse

4. Before lunch I have _____ and _____. The first is interesting, but the other
   atemhicstam   ortshiy

   is _____.
   binorg

6. After lunch, I have _____ class. Last week I forgot my _____ paper.
   cenesic   morekohw

   The teacher gave me two extra _____.
   sixersece

6. I work in the _____ the last hour of the day.
   rabrily

7. Some days after school I go to the _____ to buy _____
   obsetrook   tookbones

   and _____. Other days my _____ and I _____ soccer.
   sincelp   metscasals   catprice

Note: Did you remember capital letters?!

17. OCCUPATIONS

DIRECTIONS: Read the descriptions below and fill in the crossword puzzle.

Across

One who:
3. delivers packages
6. plans meals
10. helps when you are sick
11. builds houses
12. paints
13. treats teeth
14. delivers milk
15. works in a garden

Down

One who:
1. works with electricity
2. keeps accounts
4. plans buildings
5. takes pictures
7. works on a farm
8. sells things
9. writes for a newspaper

18. SIGNS

DIRECTIONS: Draw a line between the sign and its meaning.

picnic area

stop

railroad crossing

yield

no smoking

pedestrian crossing

handicapped

no left turn

telephone

school crossing

go

no animals

poisonous

ladies' room

men's room

19. FOLLOWING DIRECTIONS

DIRECTIONS: Follow the directions below the map. Answer the questions that follow. Then fill in the last blanks at the bottom. Are you correct?

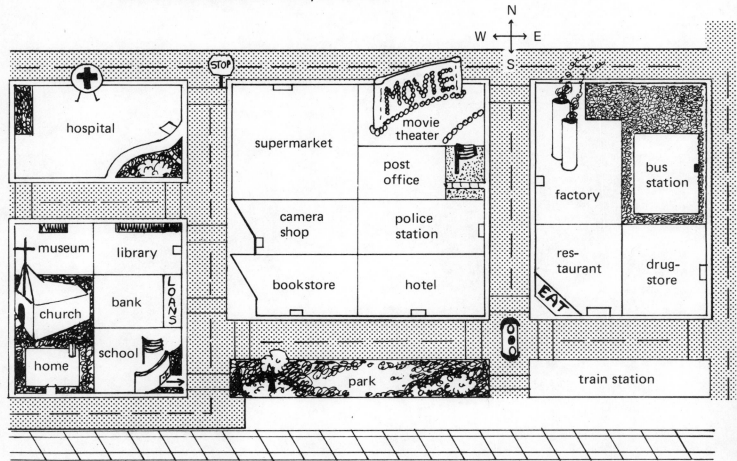

Start at school. Walk north. Turn right at the first corner. Walk two blocks and turn left. Go into the first building. When you come out, walk north again. Turn left at the first corner. Turn left at the next corner. Go into the second building on your right. When you come out, walk south. Turn right at the first corner. Go into the second building on your right. When you come out, continue to your right. Turn left at the first corner. Then turn right at the next corner. Go into the second building on your right.

Which buildings did you go into?

— — — — — — — — —
1 2 3 4 5 6 7 8 9

— — — — — — — — — —
10 11 12 13 14 15 16 17 18 19

— — — — — — — —
20 21 22 23 24 25 26 27 28

Where are you now?

— — — —
29 30 31 32

— — — — —!
2 17 4 29 6

20. PRODUCTS AND STORES

DIRECTIONS: Match each store with a product you can buy there. Write the correct letter in the blank next to the store.

Example: __Z__ shoe store   Z. shoes

1. _____ supermarket   A. stamps
2. _____ bookstore   B. camera
3. _____ drugstore   C. chair
4. _____ post office   D. watch
5. _____ photo supply store   E. brush
6. _____ hardware store   F. bread
7. _____ paint store   G. aspirin
8. _____ candy store   H. books
9. _____ jewelry store   I. meat
10. _____ sporting goods store J. hammer
11. _____ furniture store   K. chocolate
12. _____ bakery   L. basketball

21. HOLIDAYS

DIRECTIONS: Circle the word or words that do not belong with the others.

Example: Christmas   December   tree   (hot dogs)

1. New Year's   midnight   money   party
2. February   animals   Valentine's Day   cards
3. Irish   purple   March   St. Patrick's Day
4. fireworks   July Fourth   picnics   gifts
5. June   Halloween   costumes   pumpkins
6. office   Thanksgiving   family   turkey
7. flowers   May   Mother's Day   red
8. tricks   April Fool's Day   vacation   April
9. Easter   church   eggs   snow

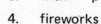

22. SPORTS

DIRECTIONS: Match each sport with the correct equipment for it. Draw a line from the name of the sport to the picture.

football   volleyball

basketball   track

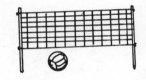

tennis   swimming

baseball   roller-skating

golf   ice-skating

soccer   boxing

hockey   fishing

ping pong   gymnastics

racquetball   diving

badminton   skiing

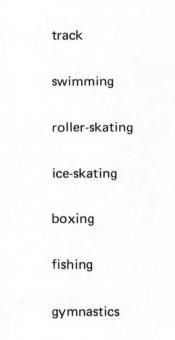

23. IRREGULAR PAST TENSE

DIRECTIONS: Write the correct form of the verb in parentheses in the blank. Then look for your answer
in the puzzle and circle it.

Example: My brother _____slept_____ late this morning.
                                        (sleep)

1. I _____ her a letter last week.
        (write)

2. The old man _____ stories about his home last night.
                        (tell)

3. My friend and I _____ to the movies yesterday.
                        (go)

4. Herb _____ a bad grade on his last report card.
            (get)

5. Tom _____ coffee with his donut this morning.
            (drink)

6. She _____ me her telephone number again.
            (give)

7. We _____ the directions that he sent.
            (understand)

8. Rosa _____ a toothache last night.
            (have)

9. The students _____ late to class yesterday.
                        (come)

10. I _____ too much this morning.
            (eat)

11. She _____ quietly when they called.
            (speak)

12. Ken _____ all the answers last week.
            (know)

13. We _____ the Abominable Snowman last winter.
            (see)

14. The class _____ early today.
                (begin)

15. Rita _____ the wrong page yesterday.
            (do)

```
U Z D O T U N H L M
A N I K P S G A V E
B Y D N Q R X D K M
F A T E T O R W J A
C M L W R K J I W C
D W V U P S N O E I
E R S T Q P T A N T
F H G S F O G O T O
G D R A N K C B O L
H E D W B E G A N D
```

24. TRANSPORTATION

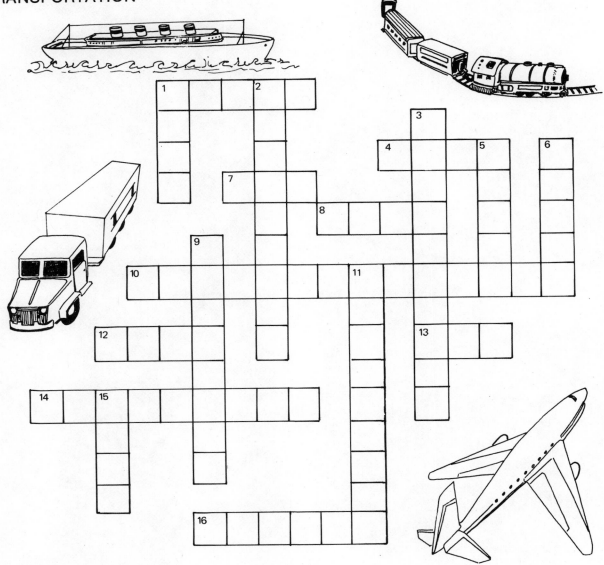

Across

1. vehicle that carries things
   (larger than a car)
4. something to go fishing in
7. transportation to school
8. another word for car
10. permit to drive
12. transportation across the ocean
13. Ford is a kind of _____.
14. emergency vehicle
16. place to park a car

Down

1. vehicle that has a meter
2. person who drives a limousine
3. two-wheeled vehicle with a motor
5. vehicle that runs on tracks
6. animal used for transportation
9. vehicle that flies
11. wealthy person's car
15. vehicle with two wheels

25. ENGLISH-SPEAKING COUNTRIES

DIRECTIONS: Unscramble the letters to make names of English-speaking countries. Then put the
names in the puzzle.

1. ewn ezdanal   _____

2. lerinad   _____

3. daanac   _____

4. nalcstod   _____

5. gelnand   _____

6. atrusaali   _____

7. sua   _____

8. adini   _____

Note: Did you remember capital letters?!

26. TWO-WORD VERBS

DIRECTIONS: Fill in the blanks with an appropriate word from the bottom of the page. Then write the
word in the puzzle. You will have to use some words more than once. The arrow points to a
hidden description of these words.

Example: Turn ____off____ the radio. | O | F | F |

1. Please fill _____ the application.

2. Sit _____ .

3. Would you turn _____ the lights?

4. Write _____ the words when I say them.

5. Why don't you take _____ your coat?

6. Follow _____ with your ideas.

7. Peggy turned Mark _____ for a date.

8. Look _____ your answers.

9. Come _____ at 7 o'clock.

10. Did you look _____ the book?

11. Why don't you come _____ for dinner tonight?

down   out
for   over
off   through
on   back

hidden description

27. GOOD, BETTER, BEST

DIRECTIONS: Fill in the blanks with the correct form of the word in parentheses. Then write the numbered letters in the puzzle.

Example: Sears Tower is the <u>t</u> <u>a</u> <u>l</u> <u>l</u> <u>e</u> <u>s</u> <u>t</u> building in the world. (tall)

1. Rocky is the __ __ __ __ __ __ __ __ __ man in the world. (strong)
   1   2 3

2. That dog is the __ __ __ __ __ pet we've ever had. (bad)
   4 5

3. Mrs. Allen has the __ __ __ __ __ __ __ __ house in town. (clean)
   6   7 8 9

4. He's the __ __ __ __ __ __ __ man in the country. (rich)
   15   16 17

5. This is the __ __ __ __ car I've ever had. (good)
   18 19 20

Example: Are you __ __ __ __ __ __ than your wife? (busy)

6. Is Laura __ __ __ __ __ __ __ than her sister? (thin)
   10 11 12 13   14

7. She is __ __ __ __ __ __ __ than she looks. (young)
   24 21   22 23

8. This summer is __ __ __ __ __ than last summer. (dry)
   25

9. This car is __ __ __ __ __ __ __ __ __ __ __ than the other. (valuable)
   26   27   28

	25	1	8	10		18	22	6	12	17	27	19				
3	27	14	23	24	20	16	15	13	2		24	26	21		11	28	7	5

Name _____ Date _____ Master 24

28. DRUGSTORE

DIRECTIONS: Unscramble the letters to make words that complete the paragraph. Write each word in the blank.

Example: Let's go to the _____drugstore_____.
                                    rudgortes

In the United States, many things are sold in a drugstore. If your friend has a birthday,

you can buy a _____. If you want to know the date, you can buy a
                    hitrabdy drac

_____. If you want to read, you can buy _____,
        rencalda   omcic sobok

_____, and _____. If you're hungry, you can buy
        sagemazin   rewnsseppa

_____ or _____. If you want to write a friend, you can
        dynca   cei merca

get a _____ or some _____. If you want to listen to
            dorscapt   penosveel

music, you can look for a _____. If you want to get up on time, get an
                                    coderr

_____. If you need change, ask the _____. Sometimes
        ralam lokcc   chirase

there is a _____, and you can buy things very _____.
                    laes   lpeachy

If you have a headache, you can even buy _____ at the drugstore.
                                                            pinsira

© National Textbook Company

29. TOOLS

DIRECTIONS: Make as many new words as you can from the letters in the words below. Write your new words in the blanks.

   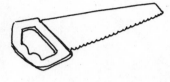

BRUSH   SHOVEL   RAKE   SAW

1. _____   1. _____   1. _____   1. _____
2. _____   2. _____   2. _____   2. _____
3. _____   3. _____   3. _____   3. _____
4. _____

HAMMER   SCREWDRIVER   TAPE MEASURE   PLIERS

1. _____   1. _____   1. _____   1. _____
2. _____   2. _____   2. _____   2. _____
3. _____   3. _____   3. _____   3. _____
4. _____   4. _____   4. _____
5. _____   5. _____   5. _____
6. _____   6. _____   6. _____
7. _____   7. _____   7. _____
              8. _____   8. _____
              9. _____   9. _____
              10. _____ 10. _____
                           11. _____
                           12. _____

30. IRREGULAR PAST PARTICIPLES

DIRECTIONS: Complete the sentences with the correct form of an appropriate verb from those listed at the bottom of the page. Some words may be used more than once.

Example: Has Chuck _____fallen_____ asleep again?

1. Have you _____ today's newspaper? The rock group Soul has _____ a new record. They have _____ their newest song every night at their concerts. Fans have _____ in line for hours to buy tickets and have _____ $10 each for them. Have you _____ any?

2. I've _____ my gloves. Have you _____ them? I hope so. They're my best pair. I've _____ them every day this winter.

3. My sister has _____ too much time to be with her boyfriend. She's really _____ behind in her studies.

4. My aunt has _____ in an airplane many times, but she's _____ nervous every time. She has _____ magazines to read. She has _____ her prayers. She has _____ the curtains on the window. She has _____ talking to the person in the next seat. Nothing has worked.

5. Greg has _____ to set his alarm every day this week. He has _____ late every day.

be	fly	pay	sleep
bring	forget	read	stand
buy	keep	say	take
fall	lose	shut	wear
find	make	sing	

31. SOCIAL LIFE

DIRECTIONS: Find the underlined words in the puzzle and circle them.

Michelle is going to give a <u>party</u> after the basketball <u>game</u> on Friday night. She has invited <u>thirty</u> <u>classmates</u>. She is planning to serve <u>pizza</u>. Her brother said she could borrow his <u>stereo</u>. Rita will bring her <u>records</u>, and Mike is going to bring his tape <u>recorder</u> and his best <u>tape</u>. Flora might bring her <u>guitar</u>. Most of the students will <u>dance</u>. No one is coming with a <u>date</u>. Since Tony has his <u>license</u> and a <u>car</u>, he can <u>drive</u> some of the students to Michelle's.

```
M F D P I N L G C R A
S C L A S S M A T E S
T H I R T Y H M O C R
O A C T D E E E E O A
R Z E Y G P R C A R T
J Z N K A E V I R D I
P I S T T D A N C E U
B P E S D R O C E R G
```

32. NEWSPAPER ADS

DIRECTIONS: Replace the shortened forms of words underlined with the words they stand for. Then fill in the blanks at the bottom of the page.

Example: Everything 4 sale.   f o r

FOR SALE

8 rm. hse. w/4 BRs, brkfst. rm., & fam. rm. w/frplc.
3000 sq. ft. 2 car gar. Near shopping ctr. and trans.
$70,000

```
— — — —          — — — — —
2                11

— — — —  — — —   — — — — — — — —
24 31            21

— — —            — — — —
27               8

— — — — — — — — — —
26

— — — — — — —    — — — —
17               5

— — — — — — — — — —
30
```

FOR RENT

4 rm. apt. w/wshr. & dryer. Crpt. in liv. rm. & BR.
1st flr w/storage in bsmt.
$250/mo.

```
— — — —          — — — — — — — — —
13               22

— — — — —        — — —   — — — —
28               23    18

— — — —
1

— — — — — —
14

— — — — —
9

— — — —
19
```

WANTED

Bldg. 15 min. N. of town for store. Call 777-1234
days or eve.

```
— — — — — — —
6

— — — — — —
25

— — — —
10

— — — — — — —
29
```

FOR SALE

1970 Ford. 4 dr. sdn. 50,000 mi. 15 mpg. A/c.
New tires. Best offer.

```
— — — —
3

— — — — —
7

— — — — — / — — — / — — — — —
15          20

— — — / — — — — — — — — — — —
12                        4
```

```
— — — — — — — — — — — — — — — — — — —
8 30 13  23 7 12 26 1 19 3  17 5  8 25 28 29 20 4

— — — — — — — — — — — — — — — — — — .
31 6  16 10 15  27 11 24 21 22 9  18 14 2
```

33. EXPRESSIONS

DIRECTIONS: Fill in the blanks with a word which will complete the common expression in each sentence.

Example: They are as different as <u>n i g h t</u> and day.

1. The Smiths fight like cats and _ _ _ _.

2. I looked high and _ _ _ for my camera.

3. Traffic at rush hour is always _ _ _ _ and go.

4. They mix like oil and _ _ _ _ _.

5. He walked _ _ _ _ and forth all evening.

6. They will stay together through thick and _ _ _ _.

7. The kids ran in and _ _ _ of the house all day.

8. I walked up and _ _ _ _ those stairs fifty times yesterday.

9. He gave money away right and _ _ _ _.

10. It's a give and _ _ _ _ situation.

11. That's the long and the _ _ _ _ _ of it.

12. They come and _ _ whenever they want.

34. FEELINGS

DIRECTIONS: Make as many new words as you can from letters in the words below.

BORED   INTERESTED   ANGRY   PLEASED   WORRIED

1. _____	1. _____	1. _____	1. _____	1. _____
2. _____	2. _____	2. _____	2. _____	2. _____
3. _____	3. _____	3. _____	3. _____	3. _____
4. _____	4. _____	4. _____	4. _____	4. _____
5. _____	5. _____	5. _____	5. _____	5. _____
6. _____	6. _____	6. _____	6. _____	6. _____

35. JOB HUNTING

DIRECTIONS: Use the clues below to fill in the crossword puzzle.

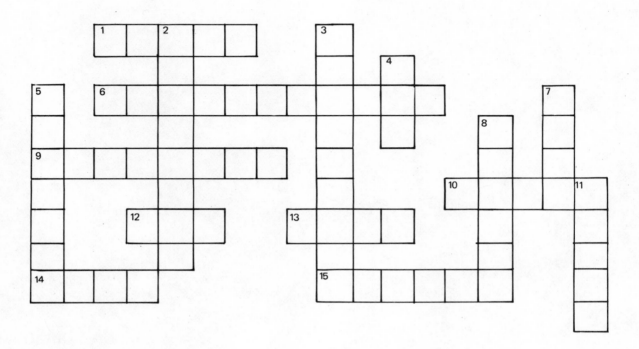

Across	*Down*
1. On payday you get a _____.	2. one who works for another
6. the form you fill out to get a job	3. a meeting with an employer before you get a job
9. the person you work for	4. another word for work
10. The day I was born is my _____ date.	5. Saturday and Sunday
12. male/female	7. "I can't work full time, but I can work _____ time."
13. another word meaning "to employ"	8. 5'9"
14. "I can't work nights, but I can work _____."	11. 4 pm–8 pm daily
15. 157 lbs.	

36. OTHER WAYS OF SAYING THINGS I

DIRECTIONS: For each sentence find the word(s) from the list at the bottom of the page that means almost the same thing as the underlined word(s). Write your answers in the blanks at the left.

_____ 1. He left the burning building in a hurry.

_____ 2. Did Randy telephone you?

_____ 3. You'll improve fast with medicine.

_____ 4. She returned to work.

_____ 5. Please complete the form.

_____ 6. The detective searched every room in the house.

_____ 7. She entered the taxi gracefully.

_____ 8. Grandmother became ill.

call you up	got in
fill out	got out of
get better	got sick
went back	looked through

37. OTHER WAYS OF SAYING THINGS II

DIRECTIONS: For each sentence find the word(s) from the list at the bottom of the page that means almost the same thing as the underlined word(s). Write your answers in the blanks at the left.

_____ 1. Give me a ring the next time you're in town.

_____ 2. Drop me a line when you have time.

_____ 3. I'm beat!

_____ 4. Do you give up?

_____ 5. I'm going to look him up when I'm in New York.

_____ 6. Drop in about six o'clock.

call me up	quit
come over	very tired
contact him	write me

38. EMERGENCIES

DIRECTIONS: Fill in the blanks to complete the paragraph. Then find the answers in the puzzle and circle them.

Example: An ___ambulance___ will take him to the hospital.

In case of emergency, you can rely on many people in the community for _____. For

example, if you have a toothache, you can call the _____. If you fall down and think your leg is

_____, you can call the _____. If you see a fire, first shout _____! Then

call the fire _____. If you see a car hit another car, call the _____ to report the

_____. You may even have to call the _____ to get an ambulance. The important

thing is to get to a _____ as quickly as possible. If there is no telephone _____, you

can call the _____ for help. Don't forget the people that live near you. _____

can always help.

```
D N O H B P M I E A
D E P A R T M E N T
F I E L O V R Q N S
I G R S K P L E H I
R H A W E X D Y N T
E B T O N I U T J N
B O O K C P H O N E
K R R C R O T C O D
G S A P O L I C E B
C H O S P I T A L F
```